JUSTIN BIEBER

STEPS TO STARDOM

JUSTIN BIEBER

STEPS TO STARDOM

JOHN KASTNER

BlueMoon
PUBLISHERS

Justin Bieber: Steps to Stardom

Copyright 2018 by John Kastner

ISBN: 978-1-988279-79-4

All rights reserved

Edited By: Talia Crockett and Allister Thompson

Book Designer: Jamie Arts

Photography: See Photo Credits on page 141

Published in Stratford, Canada, by Swan Parade Press, an imprint of Blue Moon Publishers.

Printed and bound in Canada.

The author greatly appreciates you taking the time to read this work. Please consider leaving a review wherever you bought the book, or telling your friends or blog readers about *Justin Bieber: Steps to Stardom* to help spread the word. Thank you for your support.

TABLE OF CONTENTS

FOREWORD BY JUSTIN BIEBER

I have to admit that the first time I stepped into the exhibit about myself at the Stratford Perth Museum, it was a bit weird.

An exhibit about yourself? And I'm still alive! That's what I kept thinking.

The exhibit *Steps to Stardom* was not just humbling for me; it also brought back all sorts of memories, and not just from the early part of my career but from childhood as well. The first time I went through the exhibit, I was with my mom and grandparents, and I couldn't believe that my grandparents had kept all of my stuff.

I gave my grandpa a big hug when I saw some of the things he and my grandma had kept and loaned to the museum. He won't mind me saying that he teared up. I really have to thank my grandpa and grandma and the museum for making this happen.

When the museum first asked if they could do an exhibit about me, I said, "Go for it."

Now that the exhibit is a year old, I can say that I'm really happy thousands of people have come from all over the world to visit and to enjoy seeing the stuff that means so much to me. I also want to say thanks to the people who have taken the time to write such nice messages on the blackboard.

I'm so glad the exhibit makes people happy, and that's the big reason I said "sure" when John and the people at the museum asked if it was okay to extend the exhibit another year.

I also think it is great that the museum is doing this book and catalogue. The book talks about how the exhibit came to be, it gives more information about the items on display, and the best thing is it tells some of the great stories from the first year.

Justin Bieber

STEPS TO STARDOM CREATORS
**SARA ZILKE AND MICAELA FITZSIMMONS
WITH JUSTIN BIEBER**

Steps to Stardom: The Exhibit

The *Steps to Stardom* exhibit at the Stratford Perth Museum that launched on the Family Day weekend in 2018 was several years in the making. Putting on a display about the Stratford native had been talked about for a number of years, but it wasn't until I had a conversation with Justin's grandparents, Bruce and Diane Dale, that it started to become a reality.

That conversation took place in the summer of 2017; Bruce and Diane loved the idea and invited myself and Micaela Fitzsimmons to their house to look at their Justin stuff. On the way there, Micaela, who is our manager of collection and exhibits, and I agreed that this visit would determine if we were going to do an exhibit about the native son and one of the most popular music stars in the world.

If there were just newspaper clippings, scrapbooks, and posters, the usual stuff that proud grandparents collect, we were going to politely pass. Instead, Bruce and Diane's house was in and of itself a museum. There were Teen Choice surfboards, hundreds of running shoes, countless awards, great photos, stuff from his time as a little kid, personal laptops, backstage passes, a letter from a First Lady...

Game on.

We took pictures of everything, created an inventory of all the items, and then went about building the exhibit. Micaela and I began talking about concepts and the storyline for what was going to be a fairly modest one-room exhibit.

As much as the grandparents were totally on side, we felt we needed Justin's blessing. Justin sent a text: *Go for it*. That was good enough for us.

Then emails went back and forth with Scooter Braun and his company to make sure there were no problems with playing Justin's music, showing the movie *Never Say Never*, the use of images, and where we would get Bieber merchandise to sell in our gift shop.

For the record, everyone was awesome to work with.

Meanwhile, Galen Simmons from the local newspaper, the *Stratford Beacon Herald*, dropped by to see what we were doing for exhibits in 2018. It's something they have done every fall when they are looking for copy on a slow day.

We talked about our refreshed Stratford Festival exhibit.

We were really proud of pulling together a partnership with the Monroe County Museum in Monroeville, Alabama, and we were going to have a travelling exhibit about Harper Lee, the author of *To Kill a Mockingbird*. The Stratford Festival was presenting *To Kill a Mockingbird* in 2018.

And then I mentioned that we were going to have an exhibit about Justin Bieber. It was literally the third thing I talked about.

What happened next has happened dozens of times since: we were caught totally off-guard by the incredible public and media response to news of the exhibit. The *Beacon Herald* published the story online that afternoon. Within an hour, the phone began to ring off the hook: the Canadian Press, the CBC, CTV. I came into work Friday morning and there were television crews here. Friday night I was live on CTV and CBC.

When I came into work Monday morning, the first thing I did was see Micaela, who along with our intern, Sara Zilke, was in the process of creating a small one-room exhibit. I said, "We've got a problem."

She responded right away. "I know. I just got off the phone with somebody from India that was asking about the exhibit."

"We can't have people coming here from Japan and India to see a one-room exhibit," said Micaela.

Within a couple of minutes, we decided to move the exhibit into our largest gallery, and for the next few days Micaela and Sara, and occasionally myself, hunkered down to expand the exhibit by about 1,000%. We were in touch with Diane and Bruce, we scoured websites to get ideas from other museums, and we even built models of what the exhibit would look like.

This is a museum that has never been flush with money, but from that day on money was almost no object when it came to this exhibit; we were ordering new display cases, Plexiglas hoods, projectors, monitors, even sheets of steel.

The cornerstone of the exhibit is a re-creation of the front steps of the Stratford Festival's Avon Theatre. It was there that Justin's mom Pattie filmed Justin busking and posted the videos on YouTube.

Museums are traditionally pretty quiet places, but the week before the exhibit opened was a week like no other in the hundred and some year history of the Stratford Perth Museum.

We put tickets online for the opening, which was Family Day weekend (February) in Ontario. Again, we were caught off-guard when the weekend was completely sold out with days to go.

With a day to spare, the exhibit was completely ready. We had 500 t-shirts in stock, two cash registers, lots of staff and volunteers lined up. The museum was to open at 10:00 a.m. on Sunday morning.

At 7:00 a.m. I got a text from our custodian: *Just so you know, there are people lined up at the museum.* Bruce and Diane drove through and took a picture and sent it to me. Kayla Droog, our manager of education and programs, sent a text that said, *You might want to get out here.*

I pulled up about twenty minutes later to see roughly 150 people lined up outside the door. It was -10C, the third weekend in February in Canada.

Again, from that point on, nothing surprised us.

In 2012, the museum had 853 visitors. For the year. On Family Day weekend 2018, we had over 1,000.

In 2015, the Stratford Festival mounted the *Diary of Anne Frank*, so the Stratford Perth Museum hosted a travelling exhibit from the Anne Frank House. We broke all of our attendance records that year with just over 11,000 patrons. We felt we would never have another year like that, but *Never Say Never*. In 2018, the museum had 20,000 visitors.

In April, Justin, along with his grandparents, came to the museum for the first time. He spent about 90 minutes in the exhibit, posed for pictures, and signed a t-shirt for the museum that became part of the exhibit and now hangs in our gift shop. It was a great moment for us when we saw his reaction. He couldn't have been any nicer. He said thanks half a dozen times, he asked to have his picture taken with Micaela and Sara, the two people who created the exhibit, and I took a picture of the two of us.

I had an Instagram account for a long time but had never posted anything. The picture of Justin and me was my first post, and as the expression goes, my phone blew up!

Throughout the year, the number of people coming to visit never really let up. We ran out of merchandise, ordered more t-shirts and albums, skateboard decks, laminated lanyards, cellphone covers, and key chains.

The sheer number of people coming to the museum was astounding, but what was more amazing was where they were coming from.

It was commonplace to have people here from Brazil and Japan and France, all at the same time. It wasn't unusual to have groups of people in the exhibit who had never met talking Spanish to one another, or Mandarin or German.

On a Wednesday in October we had a mother and daughter from Black-pool, England; a mother and daughter from Stratford-upon-Avon, England, who brought us a tea towel from a local school; a young woman travelling by herself from Berlin; another young woman travelling by herself from Tokyo; and a family group of nine, three genera-tions from Sydney, Australia. As we often joke, "just another day at the Stratford Perth Museum."

Every day, someone signs our black-board and includes a hometown that turns heads. Casablanca, Morocco; Churchill, Manitoba; Key West, Florida; Monroeville, Alabama; or Reykjavík, Iceland.

That is one of the reasons we put a map right by our front door, and on the way out we ask visitors to put in a pin that marks the country they call home. We have run out of pins twice, and the map quite liter-ally has pins on every corner of the map.

The number of pins from Japan, the Phil-ippines, Brazil, France, and Mexico never ceases to amaze us.

And after the exhibit had been around for a few months, we started to see patrons that we recognized as having been here at least once, sometimes two and three times, people from Florida and Indiana and Horseheads, New York.

Needless to say, we are very proud of the *Steps to Stardom* exhibit and the way it touches people, but we are most proud that Justin also likes the exhibit and finds it comfortable visiting. When he does drop in, we always try to give him his space. He has been here with family, dropped in by himself, he once brought Jaden Smith with him, and then his new wife Hailey, not long after they were married.

We know that this exhibit will not last forever, but it will be forever remembered by the Beliebers and the people who look after and run the Stratford Perth Museum. That is one of the reasons why we have put so many of the items and the narrative that goes with them into this book that will serve as a keepsake both for the museum and its patrons.

When I left the *Beacon Herald,* lots of people told me I should write a book. I always replied "Never." Well, Never Say Never.

STRATFORD PERTH
museum
Your Community. Your Museum.

An Army of Beliebers

The Stratford Perth Museum was certainly caught off guard by the interest in the *Steps to Stardom* exhibit. Within a few hours of news of the exhibit being published in the local newspaper, we were inundated with media requests.

We soon realized that this was something special for Beliebers, and we increased the size and scope of the exhibit dramatically. We also put tickets for the opening weekend on sale online, and after seeing hundreds of tickets sold in the first hour, we made the decision that people would need tickets in advance. The opening weekend was Family Day, and we were sold out on Sunday and the holiday Monday. Over 1,000 people went through the museum that weekend.

The passion was most evident when we talked to the first four people in line. We opened at 10:00 a.m. on February 18, 2018, and they had been in line since 5:30 a.m. Sam English and Stacie Francis were from Indiana, and Camille Verret and Sandrine Ally were from Montreal. The four had met via a Justin Bieber Facebook group, and they and dozens of other Beliebers had stayed in Stratford hotels the night before.

A few groups back were four people from France who had flown in just for the exhibit. People sign our blackboard and quite often put where they are from, and we have had patrons from Iran, Australia, Spain, Portugal, Japan, China, Chile, Brazil, Poland ... and that was in one week.

A few months after the exhibit opened, we received a scroll from the Bieber fan club in India. The scroll was 170 metres in length and included messages, pictures, and tributes to the Stratford pop star.

The museum also regularly gets mail for Justin that we forward on to him and his family.

Auction Shoes

It was midsummer when Bruce and Diane Dale arrived with a pair of Diesel running shoes, signed by Justin, and suggested that we auction them off to raise money for the museum.

Through Sue Orr, one of our volunteers, we were in touch with Brent Shackleton of Shackleton Auctions.

Brent created an online auction that was pretty uneventful for the first few months. The auction was set to close December 5, and even that day started with a fairly modest total of just over $600.

The bidding was set to end at 6:00 p.m., and for the last hour the bidding was nothing short of frantic and fantastic. There were a total of a hundred bids; the winning amount was $2,900.

The shoes went to Alexandra Mancini of Horseheads, New York, which is near Elmira and just south of the Finger Lakes.

Alexandra and her mom were at the museum on opening day and again for an event in July and also visited with her father.

Avon Theatre Steps

The cornerstone of the Justin Bieber exhibit is this mock-up of the Avon Theatre steps with a cutout of the Stratford native.

While artists of previous generations found fame in a recording studio, Justin's launch-pad was busking on the steps of the Avon Theatre before Stratford Festival performances. That was the inspiration for the name of the exhibit. He journeyed from the steps of the Avon Theatre ... to stardom.

His mom Pattie posted a video on YouTube; a video that was seen by current manager Scooter Braun, which led to meetings in Atlanta, to a recording contract, and to international fame as one of the top pop stars in the world.

Then and even now, it sounds like an easy route to overnight success. That was not the case. One summer Justin was there over 200 times, and with the money he made, he and his mother Pattie went to Disneyland. His grandfather Bruce Dale tells the story of having to go with Justin when he performed because other buskers would try to chase him away from this preferred spot or even take his money. Bruce admits that more than once the proud and protective grandfather stepped in with fists up.

From the outset, the Stratford Perth Museum wanted to tell the story of Justin's life, not just his career, and the Avon Theatre was an important part of both.

There was a lot of discussion about the best way to tell the story in the exhibit and what images would be used to support that story. For us there was a famous and sometimes heated discussion and disagreement between the museum's manager of exhibits, Micaela Fitzsimmons, and Doug Downey of The Image Factory.

Initially, Micaela wanted an image of the front of the Avon Theatre. Doug pushed the idea of "something 3-D." Eventually, the museum somewhat reluctantly said, "Show us."

And what you see now in the museum is an image of the front of the Avon Theatre, with steps and an overhanging marquee, and a cutout of Justin playing the guitar. This has become the museum's "selfie-spot."

We tried to keep track of the number of pictures taken there on opening weekend and stopped counting at around 10,000. That is one measureable, but the other is the reaction of Beliebers as they turn the corner and see the steps of the Avon Theatre, complete with a cutout of the exhibit's namesake.

STRATFORD

Shakespeare
FESTIVAL

IN'S BRONZE STAR

JUSTIN BIEBER
RECORDING ARTIST

PRESENTED BY THE
CITY OF STRATFORD
JULY 1ST 2011

THE BAMBI AWARD

The Bambi Award Justin Bieber won in 2011 is part of the *Steps to Stardom* exhibit at the Stratford Perth Museum.

The Bambi is presented annually by Germany's Hubert Burda Media for excellence in international media and television, awarded to personalities in the media, arts, culture, sports, and other fields "with vision and creativity who affected and inspired the German public that year," both domestic and foreign.

The award is named after Felix Salten's book *Bambi, A Life in the Woods*, and the statuettes are in the shape of the novel's title character. The original 1948 statuettes were porcelain, but since 1958 they have been made of gold.

Past winners include Sophia Loren, Rock Hudson, Michael Jackson, German footballer Franz Beckenbauer, and Celine Dion.

BROOKS STEAM CAR

The *Steps to Stardom* exhibit opened on Family Day weekend 2018, and it was a couple of months later that the exhibit's namesake first saw it. Justin was in Stratford visiting his grandparents, Bruce and Diane Dale, on Friday morning, April 27, 2018.

In addition to touring the Bieber exhibit, Justin was also interested in other artifacts, in particular the museum's Brooks Steam Car. He asked about the history of the car and its value, and if he could sit in it.

The Brooks is the only car manufactured in Stratford. The factory was at 500 Ontario Street, current location of the Bruce Hotel. The Brooks at the Stratford Perth Museum was manufactured in 1926 and was purchased by the Perth County Historical Foundation in 2007 then given to the museum in 2013.

Justin's well-known exotic car collection includes Ferraris, Lamborghinis, Range Rovers, and Porsches.

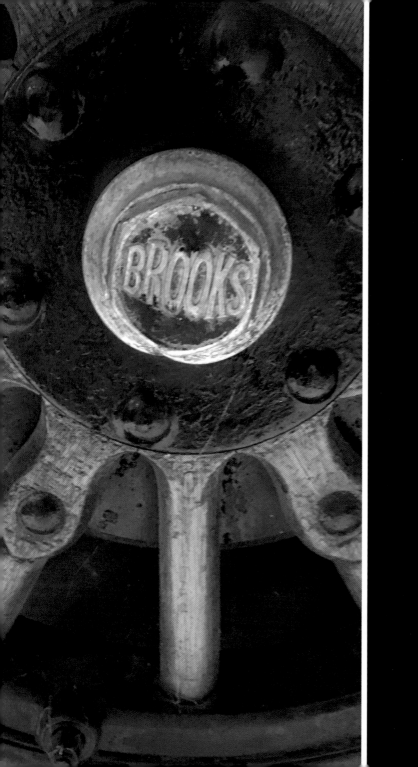

Doors Open

For some reason, we are still not sure why, we chose Family Day weekend to open the *Steps to Stardom* exhibit. Family Day is the third weekend of February, the dead of winter, when temperatures below zero and a foot of snow are the norm.

Maybe we thought that would give us a couple of months to get our feet under us before the crush of the summer season hit.

We put tickets for sale via our website thinking that would be good for people who were coming from farther away. Within minutes of the tickets going online, the sales started, and a week before the exhibit opened, both Sunday and the holiday Monday were sold out.

Friday night was reserved for the board and members of the Stratford Perth Museum, as well as staff, friends, and our sponsors, and Saturday was set aside for media.

Our plan was to open Sunday morning at 10:00 a.m., but I received a text from our custodian at 7:00 a.m. telling me that people were already lined up. Diane and Bruce Dale, Justin's grandparents, drove through the parking lot around 8:00 a.m. and sent me a picture of the lineup.

Kayla, our manager of education and programs, sent another text suggesting I get to the museum as soon as possible. I arrived a few minutes later to find there were about 150 people in line. I pushed through the crowd to get to the door and spoke to the first group. It was four young women who said they had been at the museum since 5:00 a.m.

We opened the doors at about 9:45 but had to close them a few minutes later because the museum was quickly beyond capacity. One of the first groups through the door on opening day were Thomas Dorlye, Alexandre Bineau, Alvina Ascenso, and Orlane Audiard, who flew ten hours from France. Their picture was on the front page of the local newspaper the next day.

Over the Family Day weekend, we had almost 1,000 people go through the exhibit and nearly sold out of our merchandise that we thought was going to last months.

Ellen Underwear

In the pop culture world, there are a number of indications that you have "made it," and Justin Bieber has ticked three major boxes.

Performing at Madison Square Garden — done that, and the journey is highlighted in the film *Never Say Never*.

Cover of *Rolling Stone* magazine — done that.

A guest on the *Ellen DeGeneres Show* — done that, and he has the underwear to prove it.

One of the gifts given to celebrities appearing on Ellen's show is a pair of underwear, and the *Steps to Stardom* exhibit at the Stratford Perth Museum has two pairs of Ellen underwear that belong to Justin — one white and one black.

Justin first appeared on the *Ellen DeGeneres Show* in 2009 when he was just fifteen years old, his first appearance on a major television show. Ellen has been a steadfast supporter throughout Justin's career; he has appeared on the show twenty-six times.

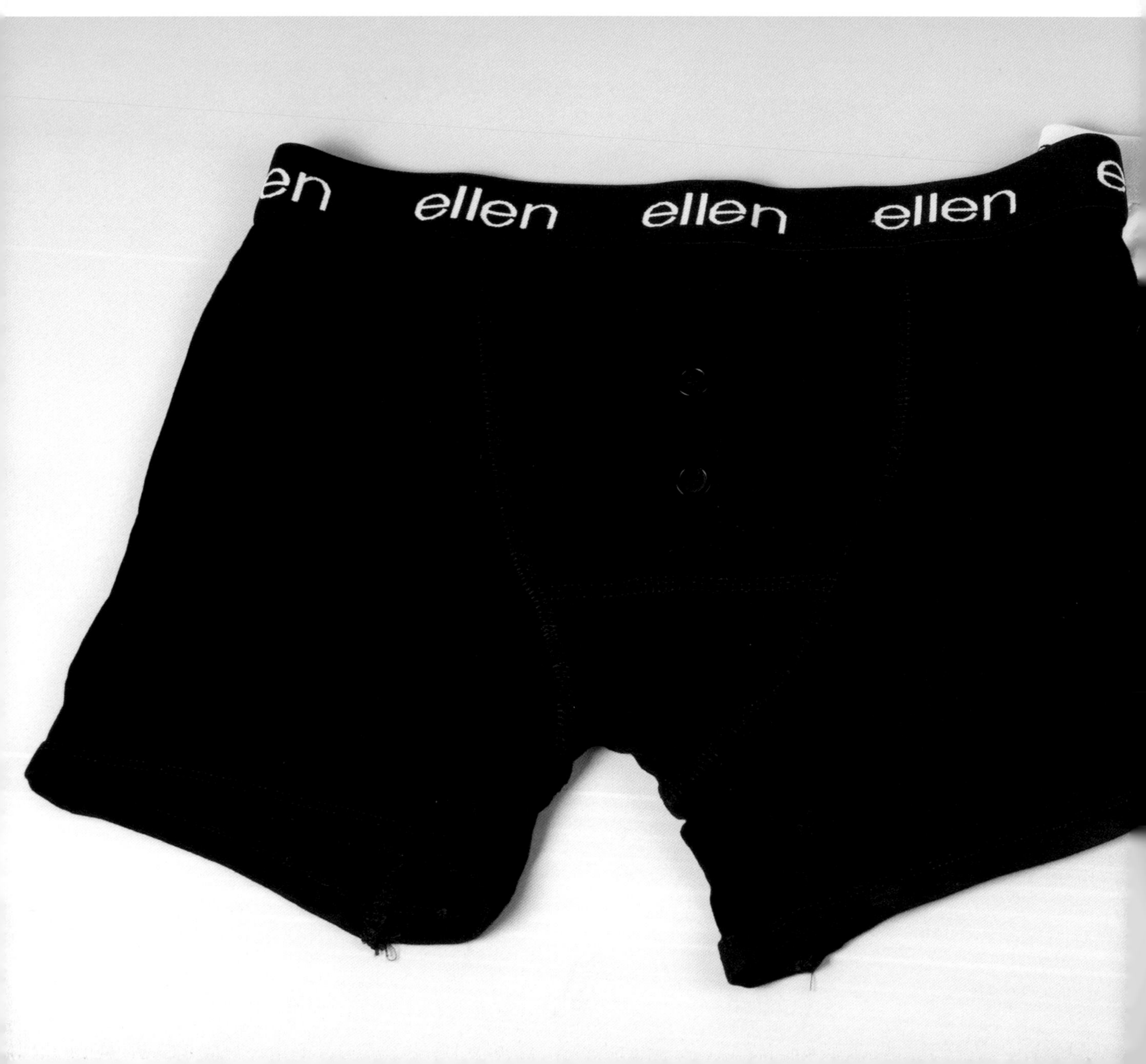
en
ellen
ellen
ellen
el

ellen   ellen   ellen   ellen

EXHIBIT T-SHIRT

Justin has been to the Stratford Perth Museum several times and usually brings people with him to see the *Steps to Stardom* exhibit. The first time was a quiet Friday morning in April 2018 with his grandparents, Diane and Bruce Dale.

We asked him if he would like to sign one of our *Steps to Stardom* t-shirts. With the help of his grandparents, he gladly obliged.

We had no intention of selling the t-shirt — we wanted to put it on display and make it part of the exhibit itself. It reads, "I loved every minute spent in this museum... Justin Bieber."

It is now framed and in our reception area. During that same visit, Justin posed for pictures with the museum staff, took a seat in our Brooks Steam Car, and signed our blackboard alongside other Beliebers.

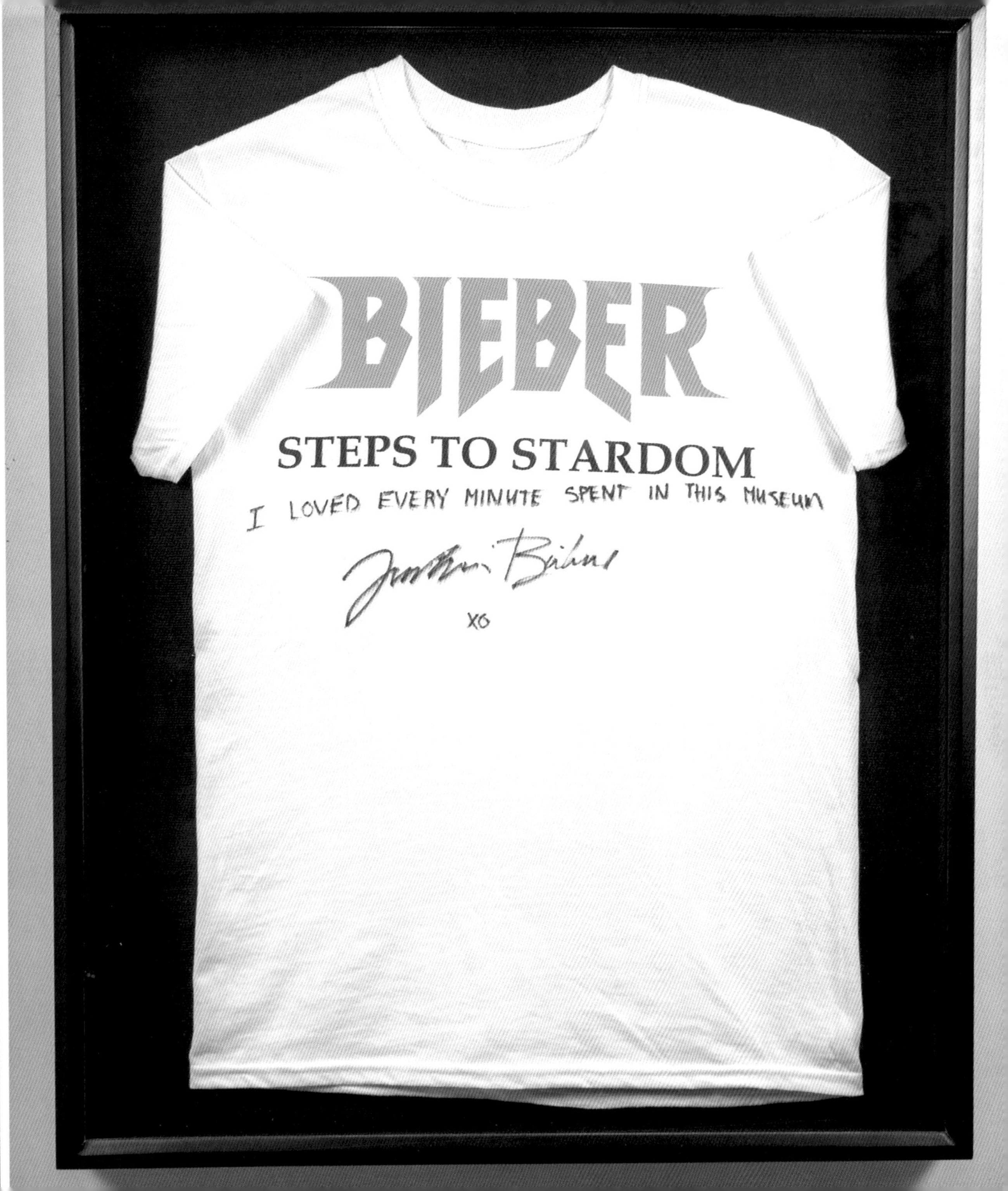
BIEBER
STEPS TO STARDOM
I LOVED EVERY MINUTE SPENT IN THIS MUSEUM
XO

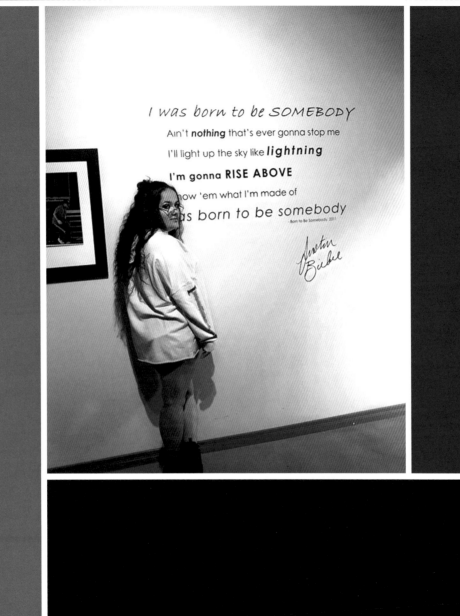

FAMILY

The *Steps to Stardom* exhibit is not just about Justin's career; it is about his life, and one cannot begin to tell that story without talking about his family. The role of family is a dominant theme of the exhibit.

There is the laptop that belonged to his mother Pattie, and the role it played in his discovery is outlined. His grandfather, Bruce Dale, boastfully talks about how he would stand guard by Justin when he busked on the steps of the Avon Theatre — not only to protect the spot from other buskers, but also to stop people from taking his money.

The exhibit itself is a wonderful testament to family, as the majority of items were saved and kept by Bruce and Diane Dale. These range from library cards to track-and-field ribbons to a hockey jacket.

Most telling is the slideshow of family photos that is part of the exhibit: over a hundred photos of Justin with his mom and dad, grandparents, siblings, and relatives.

FAN ART

The movie *Justin Bieber: Never Say Never* is a documentary about his meteoric rise from busking on the steps of the Avon Theatre in Stratford, culminating with an appearance at Madison Square Garden.

It includes home movies, backstage footage, and rehearsals, all leading up to him selling out the most famous arena in the world.

Many fans entering that concert made up signs on Bristol boards, but those signs were confiscated at the door because they are against arena policy; they block the other patrons' view.

Justin and his organizers invited family and friends to MSG for the concert, and Stratford resident Nathan McKay was among them. He saw this huge pile of posters and asked security what was going to happen to them. When he found out they were headed for recycling, he asked if he could have them. He brought them back to Stratford, held on to them for years, and when the *Steps to Stardom* exhibit was in the works, he offered up the posters on loan. These posters are shown on page 60.

It is also common for the museum to receive art — drawings and paintings of Justin — from fans.

The charcoal drawing on page 61 was done by Rebecca Stelpstra of Kelowna, B.C., when she was sixteen. She is now twenty-four and sent it to the museum with her father earlier this year. "I was studying portrait art and really wanted to do a few male celebrities in graphite. Justin Bieber had an interesting image," said Rebecca. "I remember it was hard to draw men with short hair, so I had a lot of fun with his! I remember it being a first 'win' for me with my drawings as I learned a lot from it."

Becky Willard of Rochester, New York did the two silhouette paintings shown on pages 62 and 63, which she brought to the museum opening weekend. Two years ago, she also designed a jacket that she presented to Justin.

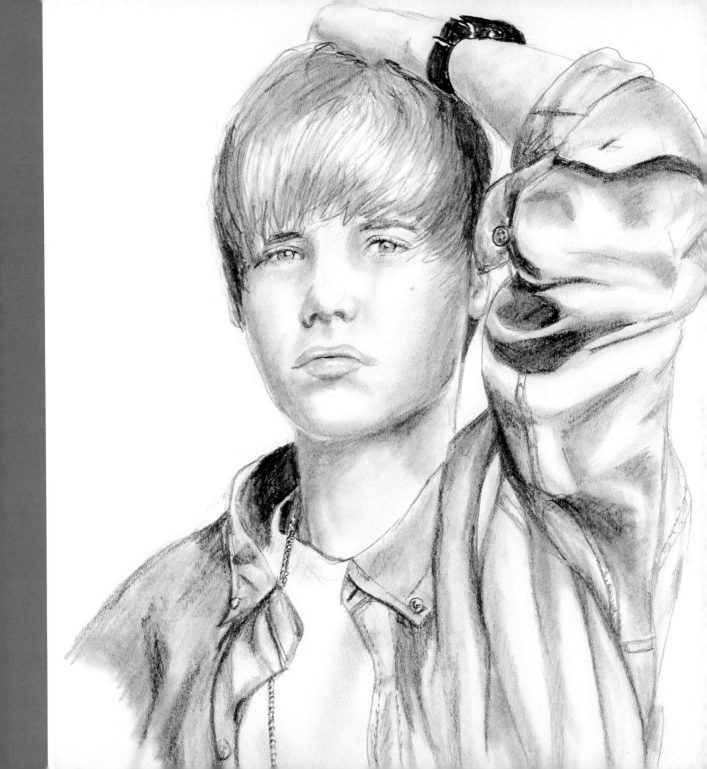

The registered card holder is responsible for all material issued on this card. Please notify the library of any changes in address. A fee will be charged for the loss of this card.

JuSTin BieBer

Signature

Stratford Public Library

19 St. Andrew St., Stratford, ON. N5A 1A2
(519) 271-0220

2 0500 00067016 1

First Autograph

One thing we know about the early Justin was that he was certain he was going to be a star. He obviously has incredible talent, but we also know he put in the work to become one of the most recognized pop stars in the world.

A lot of people were stunned by his meteoric rise, but Justin might not have been one of them. At a very early age, he was already thinking like a celebrity, and this library card is a great example. It's valuable to the exhibit because it bears one of his earliest signatures, but it is also unique because it is one of the things that came to the museum collection from someone else.

At birthday parties, while other kids were getting goodie bags, Justin would give out personal things to his friends — including this library card. After the exhibit opened, we were approached by Katie Bossers, a local resident who was a childhood friend of Justin. Katie had kept this library card; apparently Justin wasn't the only person who was sure he was going to be famous someday.

Good Canadian Boy

This blue nylon hockey jacket was worn by Justin Bieber when he was a member of the Stratford Warriors travel hockey team. That team, sponsored by Stratford Glass and Lock, was the Minor Atom MDs (Minor Development).

The great thing about the jacket is it bears his favourite sports number — 6 — which appears on lots of his jerseys, including some major sports team jerseys that were presented to him while performing concerts.

Also, there it is, right across the back: BIEBS, his nickname, even as a kid.

In the team picture, he's in the back row, second from the left. This picture is in our exhibit, and it's great to see how quickly patrons can find Justin in it.

We also have his Minor Hockey Alliance registration card. A scan of it was given to the Stratford Perth Museum by the Hockey Hall of Fame, which has the original card in its collection. Along with his library card, it bears one of his first signatures, or autographs, as they are called now.

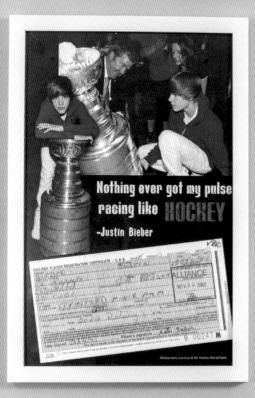

Nothing ever got my pulse racing like **HOCKEY**

-Justin Bieber

Photographs courtesy of the Hockey Hall of Fame

STRATFORD MINOR HOCKEY - 2003 / 2004 - STRATFORD GLASS & LC

FRONT ROW: ROBBIE GIBSON, JORDAN McKONKEY, JASON VINK, JOSH PINTER, KY
MICHAEL WOODEND.

MIDDLE ROW: MARSHALL METCALFE, MATT JACKSON, BREL
CHRISTOPHER DICKENSON

BACK ROW:

MINOR ATOM MD WARRIORS

EY, STEVEN SCHW...

BIEBS

BIEBER							JUSTIN						1 9 9 4 0 3 0 1

RESIDENTIAL ADDRESS

25 Kappelle

DATE OF BIRTH

CITY

Stratford

FOR BRANCH USE ONLY

PROVINCE On   POSTAL CODE N5A 6X4

ALLIANCE

TELEPHONE NO. 271-0201

HOSPITALIZATION NO.

DATE APPROVED

NOV 0 4 2003

E-MAIL

Is eligible to play for the STRATFORD MINOR ATOM

(Hockey Team name in full including Association name)

CANADA ☑

Resident at the above address since 2000   CITIZENSHIP: OTHER ☐

C.H.A. BRANCH REGISTRAR

I last registered with the following Team(s)

Please X if never Registered before ☐

YEAR: _____ TEAM: 2002 Rotary _____ In The _____ Branch/Province

YEAR: _____ TEAM: _____ In The _____ Branch/Province

I, the undersigned certify the above information to be true and in consideration of the granting of this certificate to me with the privileges incident thereto, and by signing this certificate I have become subject to the rules, regulations and decisions of the C.H.A., its Board of Directors, its branches and/or divisions which may be restrictive in some areas such as movement from team to team, conduct, etc. and I agree to abide by such rules, regulations and decisions of the C.H.A., its Board of Directors, its branches and/or divisions. I am aware that these rules and regulations are available to me through my team manager.

Date Signed Oct 4/03 ____, Player's signature Justin Bieber

This card is issued at the discretion of the Branch Executive and is revocable without notice.

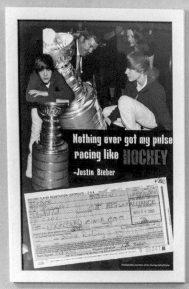

Nothing ever got my pulse racing like HOCKEY

-Justin Bieber

Justin Bieber
Duffle Bag

Justin Bieber

HOCKEY BAG

Similar to the guitar, a vintage blue Mats Sundin hockey bag for kids also found its way into the exhibit thanks to someone from the community.

Shelley Assayag contacted the museum shortly after news of the exhibit became public and told us she had something we might find interesting: a kid's hockey bag with "Justin Bieber" and his phone number of the time written on the inside.

Shelley is not sure how she got the bag; she thinks her son may have played hockey with Justin, but she knew it had been in her garage for a few years, and perhaps it belonged in a museum.

We met with Shelley and decided it would be an ideal item for *Steps to Stardom*, so we filled out the paperwork.

When we put the bag on display, we showed the name, but not the phone number. We did a quick check, and the number is in use, so we felt that it was best to keep that private.

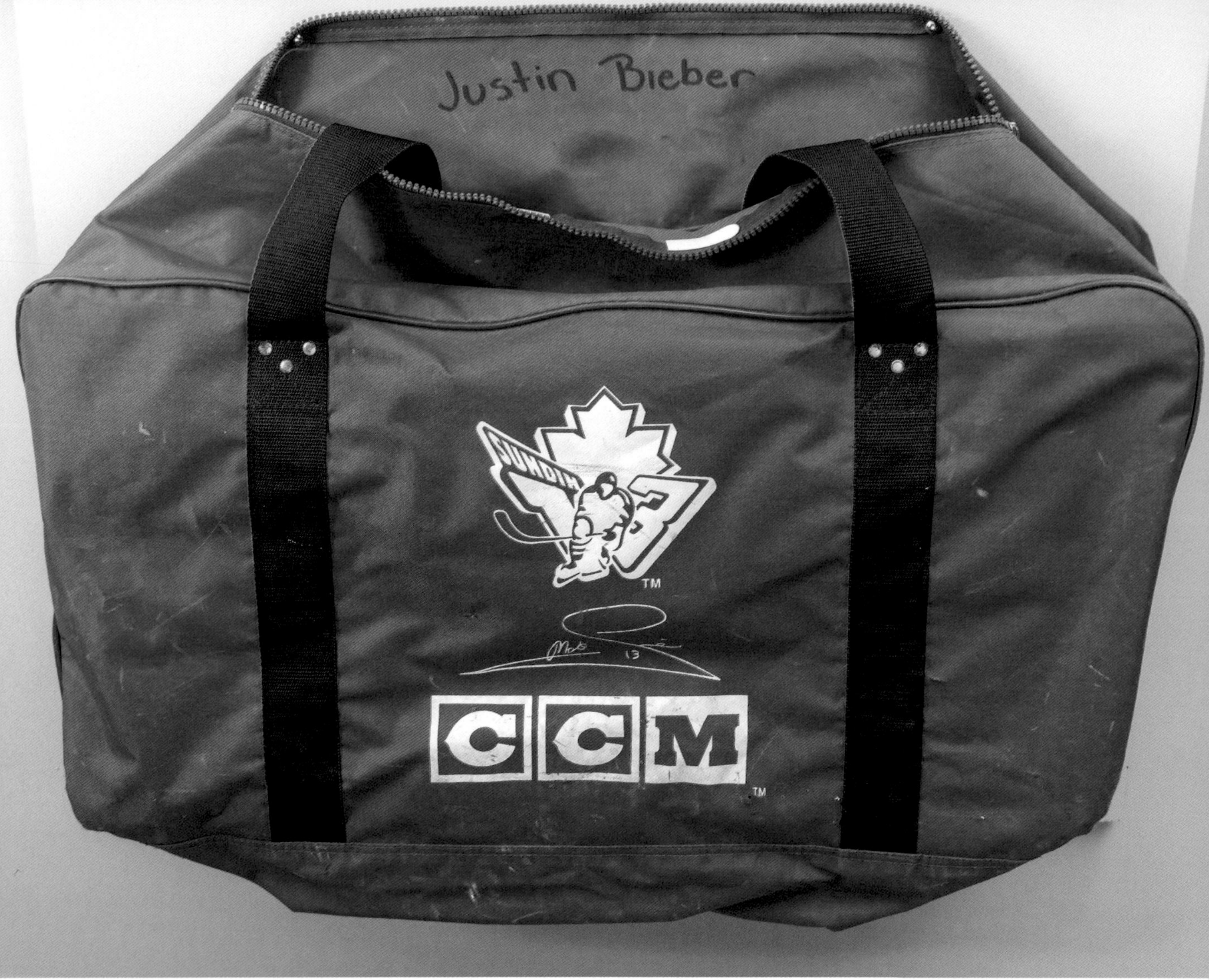
Justin Bieber
CCM

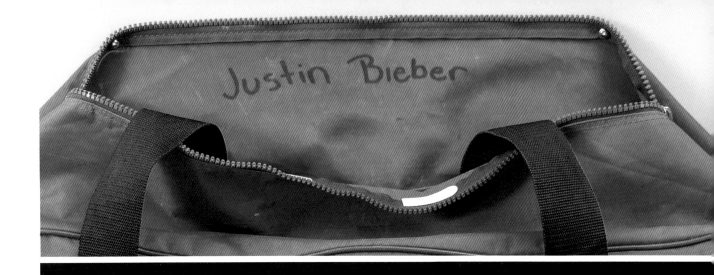

Huge Benefit – Drums

If it takes a village to raise a child, some might also suggest it takes a village to make a star.

It was 2002, and Justin was just nine years old and he would sneak into bars or the local music shop and grab a guitar or bang away at a set of drums. His talent did not go unnoticed, and some people, including Nathan McKay, organized a fundraiser at Madame T's, the former Kent Hotel.

Admission was $5, and organizers raised enough money to buy him a set of drums. At the museum there is a video of him as a kid playing those drums and of course, the drums themselves are a key part of the exhibit.

It wasn't easy tracking them down. Urban legends pointed the museum in a number of different directions, but they were actually in the possession of family friend Chad Ritter. Chad, who owns a construction company, had them in storage and loaned them to the museum for the *Steps to Stardom* exhibit.

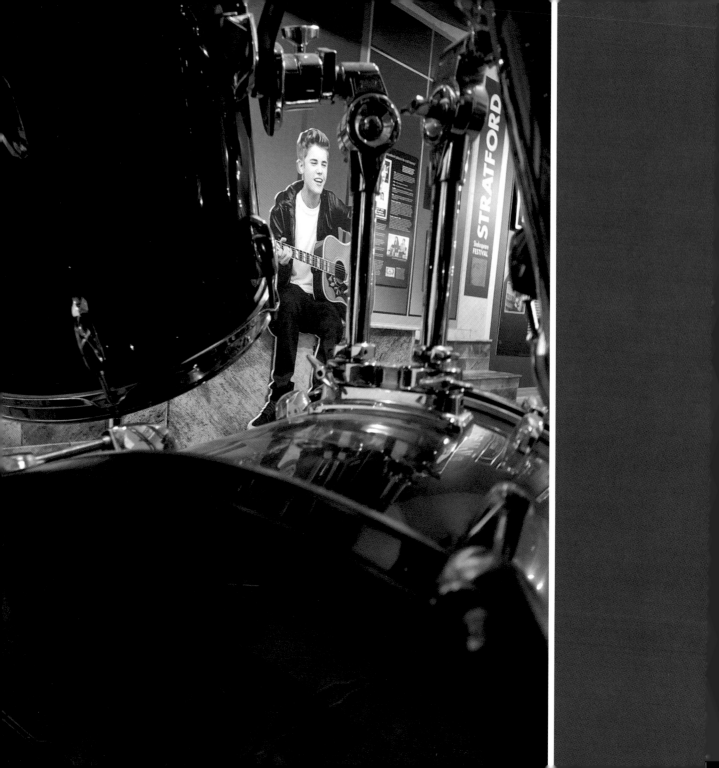

It may appear to be a case of overnight success, but it just seems that way. Long before Justin Bieber came to the attention of YouTube followers and Scooter Braun, he played music and performed for local audiences. It seemed to come naturally to him.

At the age of two, Justin was pounding out drum rhythms on the kitchen table and was soon sitting at his own tiny drum kit, playing along with the musicians that visited his home. Along with drums, he played piano and guitar, but it became clear that singing and performance were special gifts.

INCREDIBLE MEDIA COVERAGE

Like just about everything involving this exhibit, we were surprised by the media coverage. It started with a small story in the local newspaper, the *Stratford Beacon Herald*, that was posted on its website on a Thursday.

Within a few hours, The Canadian Press called and in turn sent a story to their members and radio stations, then newspapers and television stations began to put stories on their websites.

Then the international coverage began to get traction. Calvin Wood, who had worked at the Stratford Festival, sent me an email early Sunday morning from a coffee shop in New York City: *I just saw you in Billboard Magazine — I bet you never imagined in 1,000 years that you would have your name in that publication. :-) I think your Bieber exhibit is going to blow it out of the park — long term. The press you are getting on this is out of this world (I have seen multiple articles — and I am sitting in NYC).*

Regional Tourism Ontario hired a media relations firm for us to handle the requests, and Enterprise Media began setting up interviews with outlets from around the world.

Leading up to the opening, we had camera crews at the museum every day, and I did over a hundred live interviews, including about a dozen on television. We were on seven different platforms of the CBC, live on *Breakfast Television*, live on CTV, a nice feature on *Canada AM*, plus interviews in French and German.

Billboard, TMZ, ET, *New York Post*, *Toronto Star*, *Globe and Mail*, and *People* magazine all had articles about the *Steps to Stardom* exhibit.

Enterprise kept track of the media coverage, and by the end of February the number was 6,769,945 readers via print, electronic, and social media. By the end of the year, I received a 300-page media report where stories about the exhibit had more than 500 million impressions.

CTV'S *YOUR MORNING*:
BRANDON GOMEZ INTERVIEWING JUSTIN'S GRANDPARENTS
DIANE & BRUCE DALE, AND JUSTIN'S MOM PATTIE MALLETTE

CITY TV'S *BREAKFAST TELEVISION*
SID SEIXEIRO AND DINA PUGLIESE
INTERVIEWING JOHN KASTNER

Laptop That Started it All

Justin Bieber is a different kind of pop star, with a very different beginning. We know that his first public appearances were busking on the steps of the Avon Theatre in Stratford. We also know that videos of him busking, posted by his mother Pattie, led to his recruitment by major music producers.

It was on this laptop that all that took place: the posting of the videos, the emails back and forth with Scooter Braun, and the social media posts that were so instrumental in Justin gaining fans at the grassroots level.

Scooter Braun talks about this at length in the movie *Never Say Never*, which chronicles the beginning of Justin's career. He saw the video online and spent a day trying to find Pattie and get a phone number.

If Elvis and Johnny Cash and Jerry Lee Lewis got their starts and their tickets to stardom at Sun Studio, then this laptop was Sun Studio for Justin.

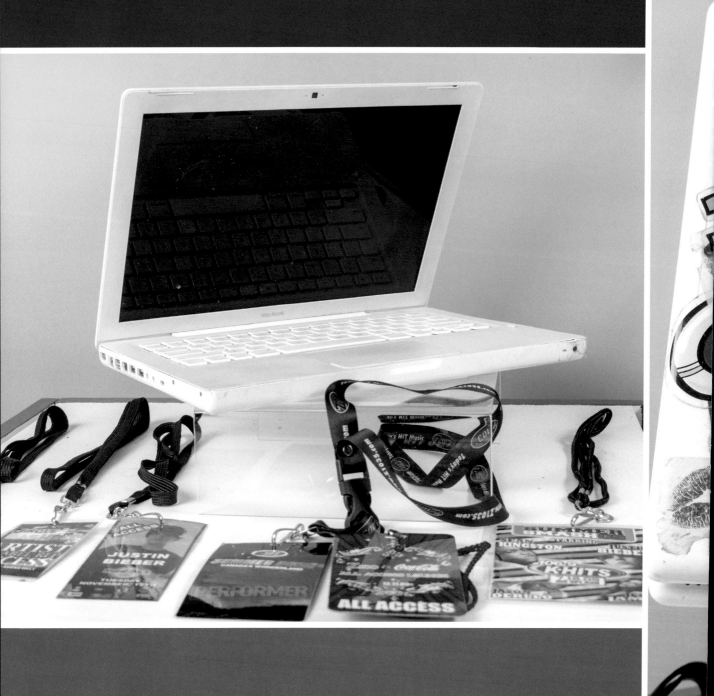

LEAVE A MESSAGE

One of the most interactive aspects of *Steps to Stardom* is about as old-school as can be.

Sara Zilke, who was an intern at the museum when the exhibit was created, suggested we have a blackboard where people could leave messages for the Stratford born-and-raised pop star. Since the exhibit opened on February 18, thousands of people have taken chalk in hand and written messages to the former teen idol, with email addresses, Instagram and Twitter handles, requests to "please call me," marriage proposals, and even references to passages from the Bible.

And patrons take great pride in writing down where they are from: "Brazil was here, Hello from Finland, Japan in the house..."

It has proven to be a very popular aspect of the exhibit and one that reaches well beyond the walls of the museum. As soon as the blackboard is full, we take a picture, post it on Instagram, clean off the board, and start all over. Most times we clean it off at the end of the day, but on weekends sometimes twice, and on opening day and weekend, it was once an hour.

Justin visited the museum on April 27, 2018 with his grandparents Bruce and Diane Dale; it was his first look at the exhibit. He and his grandparents stopped at the blackboard, and he read the entire board.

He then wrote his own message: "Justin was here," followed by a heart. We covered that message with plastic, just to make sure that it wasn't erased by accident. That was rewarding for the staff at the museum because it was an endorsement of sorts from the exhibit's namesake. That Justin Bieber message on the blackboard is also meaningful for fans who now know they are using the same blackboard. Hailey also signed when she visited with Justin, and plastic covers protect both of these messages.

The blackboard is in an area of the exhibit dedicated to fans. Across from the blackboard are posters taken from fans at the filming of the *Never Say Never* concert at one of the world's most famous venues, Madison Square Garden.

Similarly, there is a television monitor that carries the social media feed about the exhibit, as well as a huge pad of sticky notes that fans can use to write a message to Justin. As soon as that box is full, it is emptied and the messages are given to grandparents Bruce and Diane.

Laura et
Antoine
étaient là,
de France!
(From France,
with love ♡)
"Je t'aime beaucoup"
@laurabreuil

We have bieber fever Z+A
Love you -Mafer
I love yo
-Mickae
we drove 17
to be here
PAOLA, FROM BRAZIL
I ♡ U w/ all of my heart. -Kylee
Nash, TN, USA
JENNY & JACKIE
's You!
Te amo
Loves You
-Arianna

MEMORABLE VISITORS

Justin Bieber, his wife Hailey, and Jaden Smith probably take the first three spots, but there has been no shortage of amazing visitors to the museum since we opened the exhibit in February.

I think we will always remember Parnian, a sixteen-year-old girl who visited along with her mother from Tehran. They flew into Toronto, took the train to Stratford, and walked the five kilometres to the museum.

Logan and Carlee, "a couple of cool kids" who were in the Stratford Festival production of *The Music Man*, left an invite for Justin Bieber on our *Steps to Stardom* blackboard for Justin to come and see their play.

We won't forget Hans-Peter Hermann and his family from Munich. Not only were they great people, but they were almost headed to Stanford to see the exhibit until we told them it was Stratford! Upon their return home they sent the museum the nicest email.

Josie Lipnick and her mom were in the museum on a Saturday morning, having just flown in from Las Vegas. They flew into Toronto, took the train to Stratford, and also walked to the museum. Friday was Nevada Day, and all the schools were closed. For her eighteenth birthday Josie wanted to see the Bieber exhibit. They flew home the next day.

But the darkest visit had to be May 5. The power went out at the museum on Saturday morning, and after waiting it out, we had no choice but to shut the doors. But late in the afternoon the museum got a message, or I should say messages, from two young women from Oakville, Ontario, and then another message(s) from two women who were in Stratford from Toledo.

They had to go home that night but had come to Stratford just for the *Steps to Stardom* exhibit. Finally, at about 4:00 p.m., when it became apparent that the hydro was not going to come on any time soon, I met them at the museum and took them through the exhibit by flashlight and phone. By the way, the power remained out for thirty-one hours.

Finally, it wasn't a memorable visitor but a very special delivery. Lauren Petiet from Arnhem in the Netherlands had purchased tickets for the opening weekend in February.

With her family not realizing that the exhibit was in Canada, she was unable to come, and we sent her a laminated lanyard from the opening weekend. I was in the Netherlands this summer and took a *Steps to Stardom* t-shirt with me to deliver to Lauren and her mom at their home, about forty-five minutes from Amsterdam.

ACTORS LOGAN AND CARLEE,
THE MUSIC MAN

NBA All-Star Jersey

Most of the items in our *Steps to Stardom* exhibit were part of the amazing collection of things kept by his grandparents Bruce and Diane Dale since infancy. When the exhibit was in the formative stages, the first thing we did was visit Bruce and Diane and review the incredible number of keepsakes they had compiled over the years.

After the exhibit opened, Diane, Bruce, and Justin continued to bring us new things that we might find of interest, and this jersey is one of those things. There was a lot of speculation that Justin might be at the exhibit opening, but he was busy playing in the celebrity game that took place on February 17, the night before the NBA All-Star Game in Los Angeles. Because the game was in Los Angeles, one celebrity team was in L.A. Lakers colours and the other was in L.A. Clippers colours.

Justin, a game MVP in 2011, was on the Lakers team with his favourite number 6 and "Bieber" on the back. This jersey became part of the exhibit in 2019.

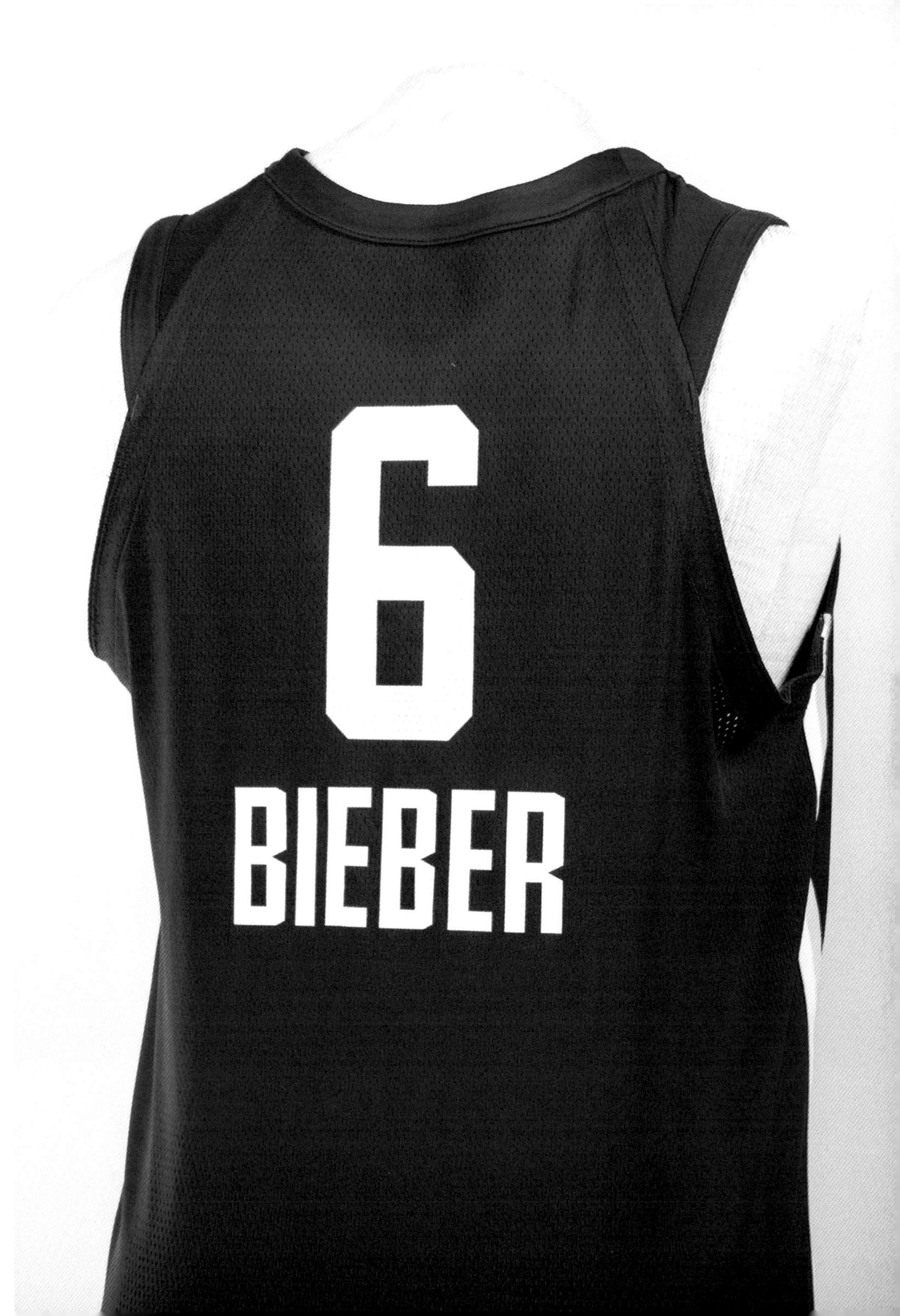
6
BIEBER

OBAMA VISIT

You know you've made it when you and your mom have a picture taken with President Barack Obama in the Oval Office.

Stanley Cup- and Super Bowl-winning teams get to visit the White House, but a picture with your mom in the Oval Office ... now, that is special. The visit took place in April of 2010, when Justin was sixteen.

He was a guest of the First Family, and he performed at the annual White House Easter Egg Roll. Also attending that day were some of the cast members of the television show *Glee* and *Harry Potter* author J.K. Rowling.

It was actually Justin's second visit to the White House. He was there in 2009 for the Christmas in Washington special, and First Lady Michelle Obama invited him back a few months later for the Easter Egg Roll.

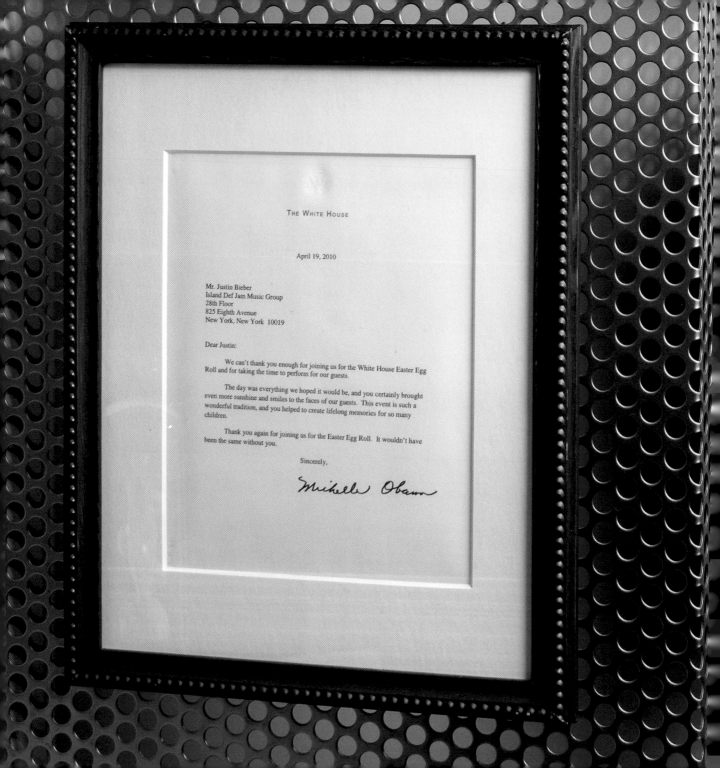

THE WHITE HOUSE

April 19, 2010

Mr. Justin Bieber
Island Def Jam Music Group
28th Floor
825 Eighth Avenue
New York, New York 10019

Dear Justin:

We can't thank you enough for joining us for the White House Easter Egg
Roll and for taking the time to perform for our guests.

The day was everything we hoped it would be, and you certainly brought
even more sunshine and smiles to the faces of our guests. This event is such a
wonderful tradition, and you helped to create lifelong memories for so many
children.

Thank you again for joining us for the Easter Egg Roll. It wouldn't have
been the same without you.

Sincerely,

Michelle Obama

Scroll From India Beliebers

In early May, after weeks of back and forth with Micaela, our manager of the collection and exhibits, a parcel arrived via UPS from India. Members of the Indian Beliebers Community, which has 1.6K likes, had put together a scroll that contained messages for Justin.

The scroll, about 18 inches wide, is 558 feet long and weighs about 20 pounds.

It includes photos, messages of support, and inspiration and hundreds of thank-yous.

It is not uncommon for the museum to have visitors from India. Many of them ask about the scroll and whether they can see it. Since it arrived after the *Steps to Stardom* exhibit was finalized, it spent the first year in our collection room, but we gladly bring it out for patrons to see and take a photo.

Displaying the scroll was one of the priorities of the relaunch of the exhibit in 2019, and it became a key part of the exhibit.

Show Us Where You Live

When I was in Amsterdam this past summer, I was in a restaurant that featured a map on the wall. Visitors were invited to stick a pin in the map, marking their hometown.

Immediately, I thought that was something we should be doing and upon my return we purchased a large map and mounted it by the main door.

We asked our students to go through the Instagram images of our blackboard and look for hometowns. We scoured our guest book, which is signed by visitors, and we searched the hometowns of people who had bought tickets online and placed the first hundred or so pins on the map.

Since that time it has been up to visitors, and almost every day a new place gets pricked; we have pins marking spots all over the world.

From Portugal to Peru, from Paris, France to Paris, Ontario. There is an incredible and somewhat surprising number of pins from Japan, Brazil, and India.

It really has become one of the astounding and lasting images of 2018.

Shakespeare's School

Circa 1847

King Edward VI School
Stratford upon Avon
Re-founded 1553

Signed Guitar

The majority of items we have in our collection came from Justin's grandparents, Bruce and Diane Dale. When we first visited their home to look at their Justin items, we wondered if there would be enough to create an exhibit. When we went there, it removed all doubt.

However, one of the coolest items in the exhibit came after it was open. Long and McQuade, a music store with a location in Stratford, contacted the museum and said they had an item that might interest us.

Justin — before he was famous, of course — used to rent instruments from Long and McQuade, including this Epiphone Les Paul Special guitar. Once he became famous, they took it out of circulation, and during a trip back to Stratford, Justin dropped in and signed the guitar.

Long and McQuade felt the best place for the guitar was in the Stratford Perth Museum, not tucked away on a shelf high up. The museum was very thankful for the gesture and had a special Plexiglas case made to ensure the guitar stays secure while still viewed by fans.

MC Stage List for Friday January 19th, 2007

1. Welcome to the second night of Stratford Star – Rebecca Tompkins, short intro.
   - Becca Says thanks and talks about tobacco video ,
   National Not Smoking Week
2. Again our Judges for the night are;
   1. Steve 'Yeager' Adair
   2. Alyse Gilbert
   3. ~~Linda Barber~~
   4. Aggie Elliot
   5. ~~and Guest Judge for this week~~ Barbara 'Babs' Young
      o They will have the difficult task of eliminating 2 contestants tonight

3. Again, the contestants for tonight in alphabetical order are:

Justin Beiber
Kristen Hawley
Leah Keeley
Jenna Klomp
Samantha McKiel

4. Each competitor will perform 2 songs tonight. The randomly chosen order is;
SIDENOTES
   o one song at a time
   o judges critique after each song – contestant should stay on stage for critique
   o the list will go once through and then repeat
   o **there will be a break after the first set – to allow time for singers to prepare

1) Justin Beiber	So Sick	I Love Basketball	
2) Jenna Klomp	Dont Forget to Remember Me	Not ready to make nice	
3) Kristin Hawley	Tim McGraw	With You,	
4) Samantha McKiel	What I like about you	Landslide	
5) Leah Keeley	At Last	146	

5. Judge Alyse Gilbert announces prize winners – ie. those leaving the show

Stratford Star Judging Notes

If there is one takeaway from the Justin Bieber exhibit, it is that no one should ever be surprised by what people decide to keep.

Certainly there are some, and Nathan McKay is among them, who anticipated greatness for a very young Justin Bieber. Those who know Justin are aware of his participation in the Stratford Star contest, a local talent show for kids.

Justin, quite famously, finished third, while Stratford singer Kristen Hawley won the competition. Nathan, who followed Justin's career from the outset and helped organize the fundraiser to buy him his first set of drums, was at that Stratford Star competition.

After it was over, he had the foresight to gather up the judges' notes and keep them. He gave them to the Stratford Perth Museum, and now they are one of the highlights of our Justin Bieber exhibit.

TEEN CHOICE AWARDS

We have two of Justin's iconic surfboards that serve as the trophies in the Teen Choice awards.

The first was for My World 2.0, from 2010 when he won for Choice Music: Male Artist; Breakout Artist Male; Choice Summer Music Star: Male; and Choice Music Pop Album. In 2011 he won more Teen Choice awards for Choice Male Hottie; Choice Music: Male Artist; and Choice Twit.

Perhaps most interesting, he also won for Choice TV: Villain. In season 11 of *CSI: Crime Scene Investigation*, Justin appeared in two episodes as serial teen bomber Jason McCann.

Justin continued to win more Teen Choice awards in 2012, 2013, 2015, 2016, and 2017. In total, Justin has won twenty-three Teen Choice awards.

Launched in 1999, the Teen Choice Awards is an annual show held in Los Angeles that honours the year's biggest achievements in music, movies, sports, television, fashion, and more. The winners are chosen by fan voting.

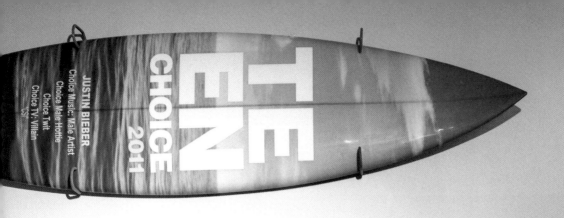

TEEN CHOICE 2011

JUSTIN BIEBER

Choice Music: Male Artist
Choice Male Hottie
Choice Twit
Choice TV: Villain
'CSI'

JUSTIN B

STRATFORD

Shakespeare
FESTIVAL

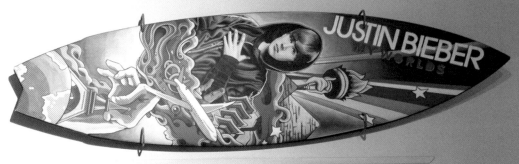

Baby, Baby, Baby...

Pattie Mallette and Jeremy Bieber welcomed their son Justin Drew Bieber into the world in March 1994.

Friends and family have always been an essential part of Justin's life, so visits back to his hometown of Stratford are a welcome retreat from life on the road.

MR. JUSTIN BIEBER
c/o STRATFORD PERTH MUSEUM
4275 HURON ROAD
RR. #5
Stratford, ON
N5A 6S6
CANADA

WE'VE GOT MAIL

Right after the Justin Bieber exhibit opened, we started getting mail for Justin. That was in part because the exhibit opened at the end of February, and his birthday is in March, so we had lots of birthday cards.

It's fairly common for us to get mail for Justin or his family, and we always pass it on to his grandparents.

In late November, we experienced a first when a Stratford florist delivered a lovely bouquet of roses — one red, one white, and one pink, and those colours had special significance.

They came with a sentimental card that had a message of faith and love from an anonymous person in the United States and were for Hailey and Justin in honour of their recent marriage.

The day after the flowers arrived, we got a phone call from the sender, and we assured them that we had been in touch with Justin's family about the very kind and touching gesture.

WOW — THAT COAT!

Justin Bieber appeared on *The Today Show* on November 23, 2011, before thousands of fans in New York City. He performed his hit "Never Say Never" and then songs from his holiday album, *Under the Mistletoe*.

But it might have been his jacket that garnered just as much attention. He was wearing a Junya Watanabe varsity jacket made of wool and leather. In 2011, that jacket retailed for $1,650 USD.

As part of our exhibit, we show the video of him performing on *The Today Show* and then, when you turn around, there is the Junya Watanabe jacket, signed by Justin himself.

THE STRATFORD PERTH MUSEUM

On the surface, the Justin Bieber exhibit at the Stratford Perth Museum is a remarkable change of direction for any museum, let alone a community museum in a small city that is in the centre of a predominantly rural county.

But it's actually a culmination of a series of fortunate events, friendships, and partnerships that began about five years ago with a call from the Stratford Festival. That conversation resulted in the museum displaying the *First Folio*, the complete and original works of The Bard, William Shakespeare.

To put it in perspective, one needs to know that the Stratford Museum has been around for over a hundred years in one form or another. It started in the basement of the Stratford Public Library, and all the good old stuff that should be kept was stored there for many years.

After that, the museum had what can be best described as an often troubled and nomadic existence with the artifacts and the museum itself in a number of locations, but that changed in 2008 when the Stratford Perth Museum Association purchased the current museum property about 300 metres west of the Stratford city limits.

That wasn't the end of the problems, however. The association, which was run by a board and only partly funded by the City of Stratford and the County of Perth, had purchased an old and historic house to be the cornerstone of the museum.

The next step was an ambitious expansion of almost 10,000 square feet that would provide the museum with galleries, an education area, and storage for its collection of artifacts.

There was a successful capital campaign that drove the expansion, but they were also counting heavily on a huge grant from the federal government.

When it didn't come through, the museum was in real trouble.

With its existence in question, the leadership of the museum went to the city and to the county and worked out a new funding agreement. Fortunately, the two governments were sympathetic, and the museum's debt was consolidated with, as the bank would say, a manageable monthly payment.

That put the museum on reasonable and stable financial ground, but there was still a big problem. The museum just wasn't that popular — very few people knew where it was and even fewer were visiting.

The same brave and bold board decided a significant change in direction and philosophy was in order, and that included a change in the staff leadership. The museum conducted a wide search for a new leader, and that search included an ad in the *Globe and Mail*. They were also going to change the person's title from curator to general manager.

That's where I come in. I had spent thirty-three years in the newspaper industry and took a buyout December 1, 2011, a few weeks after my fifty-fifth birthday. In the spring of 2012, I was more or less looking for work.

Even though I was a journalist by trade, I had a degree in English and History and was and remain a "historian." I had always advocated for the museum when I penned editorials for the local paper.

Legend has it that nearly everyone who was interviewed for the job came from a museum environment — except the recovering journalist.

But in keeping with the philosophy and the belief that the museum had to do something very different, I was hired. The joke from one of my kids at the kitchen table was, "Don't you have to have been to a museum before you can run one?"

My mandate was to first and foremost run the place but also to make the museum "relevant." We weren't really sure what to do next, but what everyone did know was that what had been done in the past few years, even decades, was not working.

You can cite that worn-out phrase about the definition of insanity here, if you like.

The need to take a totally different tack was the position of the board; I certainly agreed, and we were in lockstep from day one.

That said, I can say with complete honesty that what happened next was more good luck than the result of great vision or strategic planning on my part or that of the museum.

It was December of 2014 when the Stratford Festival called and wanted to work together.

The theatre wanted to display Shakespeare's *First Folio*, the original compilation of all of his works, but it belonged to the University of Toronto Fisher Rare Book Library, and they would let it come to Stratford only if it was displayed at a gallery or … a museum.

The museum worked out an agreement with the festival and the University of Toronto to host the book for a weekend in August. The book is worth millions, is arguably the most important book written in the English language, and we knew at the time that this was a big deal and a watershed moment for the museum.

We spent a lot of money to get ready for the pivotal forty-eight hours. We created a new gallery, installed security cameras, moved the entrance to the museum, and put our tickets online.

We garnered widespread media attention and interest, but for this to work people had to come.

In 2012, my first year at the museum, we had 853 visitors. That weekend in 2014, when we had the *First Folio* on display, we had a person a minute over two days. In 2014, the museum had over 3,400 patrons.

Boom, the museum was relevant. We had lineups, we had presented the folio without a hitch, and we were on to something. About half a million people come to the Stratford Festival every year, and thanks to the festival we were now working with them to augment the visitor experience to Stratford.

There is a great scene in *Casablanca* about a beautiful relationship, and that pretty much sums up that season.

We were poised and ready for more, and in 2015 the Stratford Festival was presenting the *Diary of Anne Frank*. We pulled out all the stops to land a travelling exhibit from the Anne Frank House and then set a Canadian record for attendance with 11,000 visitors.

In 2017, we had the foremost collection of Inuit sculptures in the world from the Art Gallery of Ontario and an exhibit about the Franklin Expedition from Parks Canada and the Royal Ontario Museum.

And in 2018, an exhibit about Justin Bieber has completely shattered all our attendance, revenue, and merchandise marks.

In five years, from The Bard to Bieber. Just like we planned it! In fact, this museum catalogue is the first in a series entitled "From Bard to Bieber."

By the way, they are both from Stratford. Okay, *a* Stratford.

Acknowledgments

The Stratford Perth Museum has had some remarkable successes the last few years. An opportunity to write about my five years at the institution and in particular the decision to present a Justin Bieber exhibit is a real privilege.

I'm a hockey person, and I always use an analogy: Sidney Crosby may lift the Stanley Cup, but there are a lot of other people's fingerprints on that championship.

Many people have made great contributions to the incredible success of the Justin Bieber exhibit *Steps to Stardom*, and by extension made this catalogue, which tells the backstory, possible.

Those contributions need to be acknowledged.

The board of directors at the Stratford Perth Museum that said "go for it" when we presented the idea of an exhibit about a twenty-four-year-old that's still alive.

Micaela Fitzsimmons, the manager of collection and exhibits at the Stratford Perth Museum, is a veteran of the industry but embraced the idea of doing something very outside the box and built an exhibit that has garnered rave reviews from patrons who have come from all over the world.

And add in that we were well into the process when a decision was made to make the exhibit about ten times bigger than we had originally planned.

During the creation of *Steps to Stardom*, we had an intern at the museum thanks to a grant from Young Canada Works. Sara Zilke, who is now a cultural programming assistant with the City of Summerside, Prince Edward Island, was at the museum for the critical six months.

Micaela and Sara were a great team, and Sara brought a new and a young person's ideas that appeal to the demographic of the *Steps to Stardom* patrons. We also had

a great corps of volunteers that painted, built cases and helped to install the exhibit.

None of this mattered without Bruce and Diane Dale, Justin's grandparents. From the outset they embraced the idea of a Justin exhibit and contributed in every way possible. They were at the museum almost every day leading up to the launch, and to say they became great friends of the museum and coarchitects of *Steps to Stardom* is an understatement. Most importantly, they became close personal friends.

Also, we could not have done this without the blessing of Justin's mom, Pattie, and of course Justin himself. The same can be said for Justin's manager, Scooter Braun. There were many points along the way when any one of these people could have said "stop, we don't like this," and we would have had to shut it down.

The cornerstone of the *Steps to Stardom* exhibit is our recreation of the steps of the Avon Theatre, complete with a cutout of Justin playing a guitar. We thank Doug Downey of The Image Factory, not just for his vision and idea, but for sticking with it even though we at the museum weren't quite sure what he was talking about. Turning that idea and vision into a backdrop for tens of thousands of selfies made this a museum exhibit for the modern age that was embraced by millennials and boomers armed with smartphones.

The Stratford Festival could also have cried foul and objected to us recreating the front of the Avon Theatre and the use of their logo. Instead, they loved it.

Kayla Droog, our manager of programs and education, and Kelly McIntosh, our administrative assistant, are responsible for what we call the front of house at the museum — that's a theatre term, by the way. Their job is to welcome people and make sure visitors enjoy the exhibit, and after almost 20,000 through the door in 2018, we didn't hear from a single disappointed Belieber.

Historically, merchandise is not a big deal for museums, and only rarely can it be tied to an exhibit with any real success, but not so with the *Steps to Stardom*. We get our merchandise from a New York City-based firm, Bravado, and they designed a number of items including a t-shirt just for us. Charles Magnan and Adelaida Echeverri are experts in retail; we clearly aren't, yet they were understanding and tolerant of our naïveté and a delight to work with.

A museum catalogue was not something we had done before, and I am proud to acknowledge the advice and counsel of

Liza Giffen from the Stratford Festival Archives. Liza sat me down and gave me straight and Scottish advice as to the difference between a run-of-the-mill publication and a fitting chronicle of the Bieber exhibit.

Pure and simple, the key was going to be the quality of the pictures, so the next call was to long-time friend and coworker Scott Wishart. Scott was a photographer at the *Stratford Beacon Herald* when I was the managing editor, and he is one of the best shooters in the country.

On a day's notice, he was at the museum, and the vast majority of the pictures in this catalogue were shot by Scott. As expected, they are outstanding.

Creating *Steps to Stardom* cost money, lots of it, many times what we had ever spent to create an exhibit.

Peter and Lisa Hyde, owners of Hyde Construction, are great friends of mine and of the museum. Finding a name sponsor for this exhibit could've been a big job, but it took one call and one short visit. The exhibit, and therefore this catalogue, was not possible without their support.

The idea of this catalogue was pitched to me and the museum by Heidi Sander from Blue Moon Publishers. It took some convincing that anyone would be interested, but Heidi was unrelenting and insistent that there should be a permanent record of *Steps to Stardom*, and now we couldn't agree more.

To all of the above, your fingerprints are all over this catalogue.

Thank you.

John Kastner

STRATFORD PERTH
museum
Your Community. Your Museum.

Photo Credits

SCOTT WISHART,
www.wishartstudio.com

(Pages 2, 8, 9, 12, 13, 26, 32, 34, 46, 47,
50, 51, 55, 61, 62, 63, 64, 67, 70, 71, 72,
74, 75, 77, 79, 84, 86, 87, 102, 103, 104,
108, 112, 115, 121, 122, 125, 127, 131,
133, 137, 143)

GALEN SIMMONS,
The Stratford Beacon Herold

(Page 24)

CORY SMITH,
*The Stratford Beacon Herold/
Stratford-Perth Archives*

(Page 5)

All other images were taken by John Kastner
and Stratford Perth Museum staff.

About The Author

John Kastner is a lifelong writer, having spent thirty-three years as a journalist. He graduated from Wilfrid Laurier University with majors in English and History, began his career as a sports writer at the *Stratford Beacon Herald*, and retired as the managing editor in 2012. During his career at the Stratford daily newspaper, he often wrote about and organized the coverage of the meteoric rise of local teenager Justin Bieber.

In 2013 he began a second career as the general manager of the Stratford Perth Museum. The Stratford Perth Museum exhibit *Steps to Stardom*, and this book, in many ways is another chapter in John's telling the story of Bieber's rapid ascent from a local kid with talent to one of the world's most popular musicians.

John is a lifelong resident of the Stratford area, a former Stratford Sportsperson of the Year, and a recipient of the chamber of commerce award for business excellence. He is very involved in sports and is the commissioner of the Intercounty Baseball League. John is also on the board of the Ontario Hockey Federation, a branch of Hockey Canada.

About The Publisher

Once in a blue moon, a story comes along that captures hearts and imaginations. We're a boutique Canadian publishing house that shines a light on diverse stories and new voices. We strive to have a meaningful impact on our readers through the books we print, and we are committed to publishing works that inspire, encourage, and motivate our readers to make the world a better place.

Swan Parade Press, an imprint of Blue Moon Publishers, carefully curates a list of books that are driven by regionally based voices and perspectives. This regional imprint features contemporary and historic stories of Stratford and surrounding areas in many literary forms, from non-fiction to fiction across all genres. We welcome submissions directed to Swan Parade Press via the guidelines on our website:

www.bluemoonpublishers.com